Angel
This totally awesome
book belongs to:
Esha

Written by
Sarah Delmege and Kirsty Neale
Illustrated by Amanda Enright

This edition published by Parragon in 2009

Parragon
Queen Street House
4 Queen Street
Bath BA1 1HE, UK

Copyright © Parragon Books Ltd 2008

All rights reserved. No part of this publication may be reproduced, stored in a retrieval system or transmitted, in any form or by any means, electronic, mechanical, photocopying, recording, or otherwise, without the prior permission of the copyright holder.

ISBN 978-1-4075-4465-6
Printed in China

GIRLS ONLY!
Girls' Night In
Parragon
Bath • New York • Singapore • Hong Kong • Cologne • Delhi • Melbourne

Get the Party Started

Awesome—you've persuaded your parents to let you have a sleepover! Now it's time to get down to some serious planning.

Make a date and time

The best day for most people to have a sleepover is Saturday. You'll have the whole day to get things ready! Aim to start partying at some point between 4 and 7 pm and ask your pals' parents to pick them up at about 10 o'clock the next morning.

Pick a place

If your room is too small, the living room usually makes a great choice. You could also eat there and have an indoor picnic on a blanket. If you're planning to give each other makeovers, head upstairs to your bedroom or the bathroom.

The guest list

Write out a list of the friends you want to ask, then check with your parents how many they're happy for you to invite along. Don't be afraid of inviting a mixture of friends.

Think of a theme

A good way of starting to plan your sleepover is to give the party a theme. If you want to give this idea a try, pick one of the themes below, or dream up a theme of your own.

Theme ideas

- Movies (in general, or one favorite film in particular)
- Chills and thrills (a spooky theme like this is especially good for Halloween)
- Jungle
- Black and white
- Disco
- A city (e.g. New York, London, Paris)
- Magic
- Hearts
- Half-birthday (throw this on your half-birthday, and give everything a half-theme—half cookies, half sandwiches, half-full glasses of drink, etc...)

Super-stylish parties

Throw a party in style with these ultra-glam top tips.

Handbag invites

Set the scene with funky, fashionable invitations. Make a handbag-shaped card, then add your party info inside.

Mega-glam venue

Roll out a length of red material, ready for your VIP guests to arrive. To give your superstar entrance even more glitz, drape some twinkly lights around the door, too.

Star snacks

Make your own fashionista drink by mixing crushed strawberries or raspberries with club soda. Then use a star-shaped cookie cutter to create superstar sandwiches and mini-pizzas.

Party on

So much to do, so little time—pack your party with loads of fun activities. Try the following out on your party pals.

Pass the polish

Sit in a circle with your pals and listen to your fave music. Hand around a bottle of nail polish. Each time the music stops, the player holding the bottle paints one fingernail. The polish is then passed around again. The first person to paint all ten nails wins.

Get creative

Rummage around for some sequins, fabric glue, and odd scraps of material. Then ask each pal to bring a pair of old jeans to your party. Put all your material together and have fun designing your new-to-you jeans again. Awesome!

Dancing queen

Pump up your fave tunes and get dancing. Why not try inventing a few dance routines, or holding a competition! You could award party prizes for the best dance act, the silliest outfit, the funniest moves—as many as you like.

Set the Scene

Get your party space ready with these top tips.

ORGANIZE IT

- Clear a space so there's plenty of room for dancing and playing games. You might need some help to move furniture.

- Not planning to sleep in your bedroom? The dance floor you've cleared will make a great place for sleeping bags later on.

- Arrange special areas for any other activities you've got planned. For pampering, set out hair and beauty products on a table along with a mirror. Let your guests know if they need to bring old clothes to wear for these, too.

- Set up your snacking corner. Ask your mom or dad to help out with the food. Stack up some paper plates and cups if Mom's not keen to let you use the family china!

Chain reaction

- Cut strips from wrapping paper or colored art paper—1 x 7 inches is a good size.
- Stick the ends of the first strip together to make a ring of paper.
- Loop the second strip through the ring, and stick the ends together again. Keep going in the same way until you've made an entire chain.

Fantastic balloons

- Write words (try "friends," "cool," or "party") onto each one in marker pen before you blow it up.
- The words will stretch and get bigger when the balloon is inflated.

Let there be light

Ask your mom or dad to dig your Christmas lights out of the attic or garage and drape them around the room for added sleepover sparkle.

Always wash your hands before you start cooking. It's a good idea to wear old clothes or an apron, too.

Get an adult to help, especially if you're using the oven, stove, or sharp knives.

PESTO POPCORN

You will need:

- Plain popcorn (already popped, or you can pop it yourself)
- 1 stick of butter
- ¼ cup finely grated Parmesan cheese
- 3 tablespoons chopped basil
- ¼ cup chopped nuts

What you do:

Ask an adult to help you melt the butter in a saucepan. Stir in the chopped basil, cheese, and nuts. Put your plain popcorn into a large bowl and pour the pesto mixture on top. Have some paper towels or napkins handy for your sticky fingers once you start eating!

Create your own cool sweet and salty snacks using the recipes on these pages. Yum!

DIY PIZZAS

You will need:

- Bread rolls • Tomato paste • Pesto • Grated cheese
- Various toppings (e.g. ham, mushrooms, pineapple, bell peppers, corn)

What you do:

- Give each person a bread roll and a plate to work on.
- Slice your bread roll in half and use the cut side as the base for your toppings.
- Spread on some tomato paste or pesto and sprinkle grated cheese on top and then add your favorite toppings.
- Put your pizzas on a baking sheet.
- Ask an adult to cook your pizzas at 400°F for 10-15 minutes, until the cheese is melted.

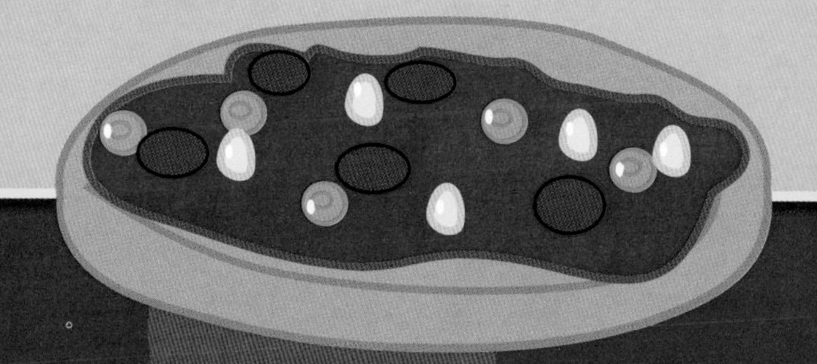

Easy recipes

Treat your friends with these yummy snacks. Yum!

Fruity cutie

Chop up pieces of strawberry, pineapple, bananas, and orange, and slide them onto kebab sticks. Serve them on a plate with a bowl of melted chocolate and get dipping.

Ice delight

Fill a tall glass with ice cream, fruit, marshmallows, and chocolates. Finish off with some whipped cream, sprinkles, and some tasty berries—yum!

Cookie sandwich

Use the back of a spoon to smear ice cream or whipped cream onto a plain cookie. Add another plain cookie on top, and you have your very own super-creamy cookie sandwich.

"My perfect sleepover is a bunch of friends, a bunch of chips 'n' dips, and scary movies!"
Jamie Lynn Spears

Truth or Dare

Grab your gal pals and get giggling with this Truth or Dare game. Close your eyes and drop your finger on one section, then do the dare or tell the truth.

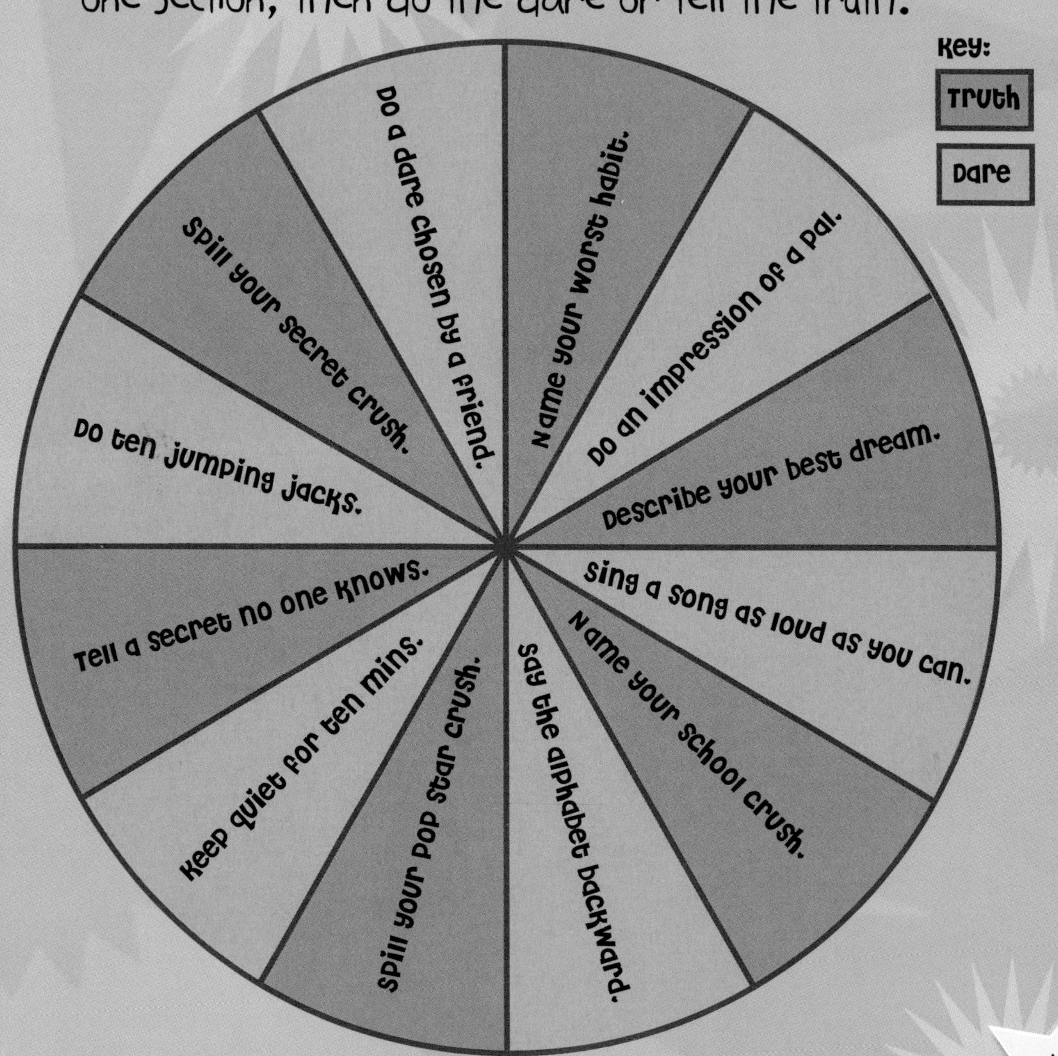

What kind of friend are you?

What's your own special role in your group of friends? Try this fun quiz and find out!

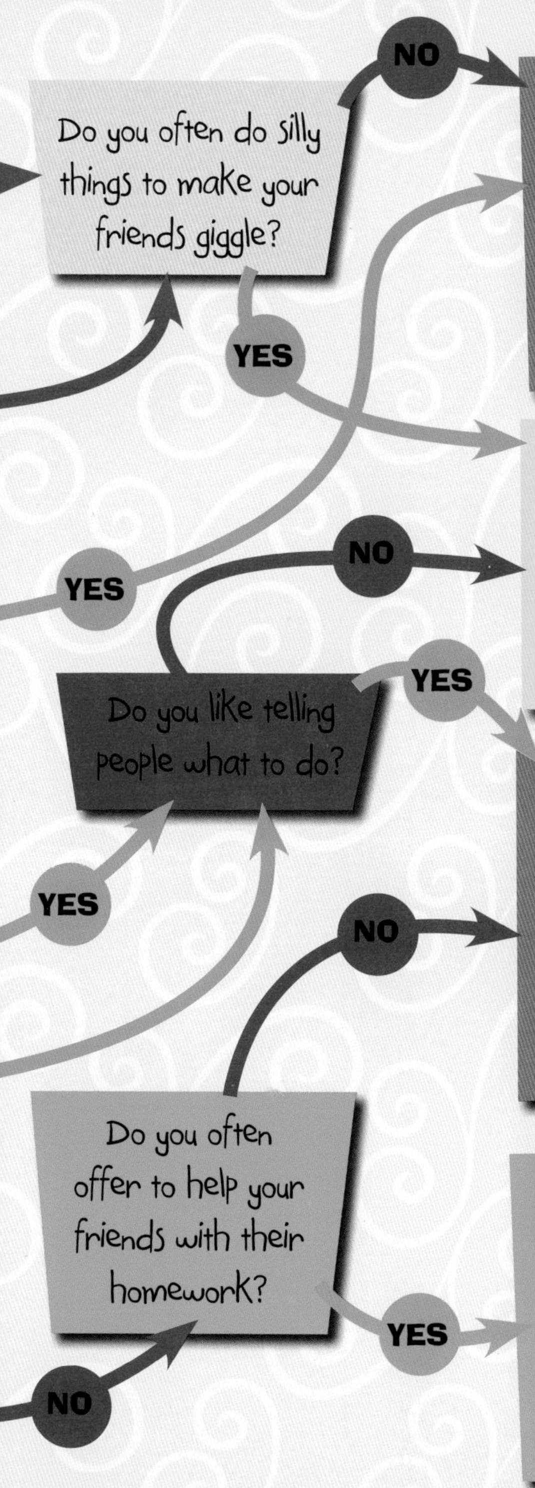

Fashion guru: You always look fantastic whether you're going to a party or cleaning out your pet rabbit's hutch! Friends admire your fashion style and are always asking you for advice and fashion tips.

Comedian: You're always the life and soul of any event. You have a huge group of friends and your fantastic sense of humor gets you and your friends out of tons of sticky situations.

Leader of the gang: You're a born leader and love being at the heart of the action. There's never a dull moment with a friend like you around. You're always organizing things and making sure that everyone has fun!

Caring and sharing: You're a real sweetie who loves helping her friends. If they ever get upset, you're right there with the tissues, offering them a shoulder to cry on and a big hug.

Gorgeous gallery

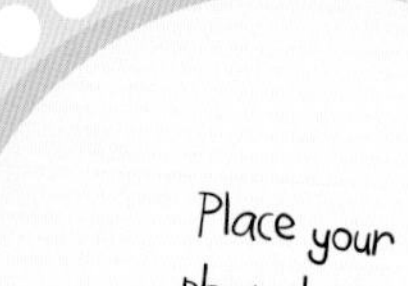

Every girl loves to look her best. Grab your pals, strike a superstar pose, and stick your fab photos in these cute picture frames.
Place your photo here
Place your photo here
Place your photo here
Place your photo here

Star factor

Grab your friends and make like superstars with this pop-tastic game.

What to do:

1. Take it in turns to be a judge and a singer.
2. Each singer must sing one song in front of the judge(s) and is given a score out of ten.
3. Then, the singer becomes a judge and one of the judges becomes the singer.
4. Once everyone has performed and been given a score, the singer with the highest mark wins "Star factor."

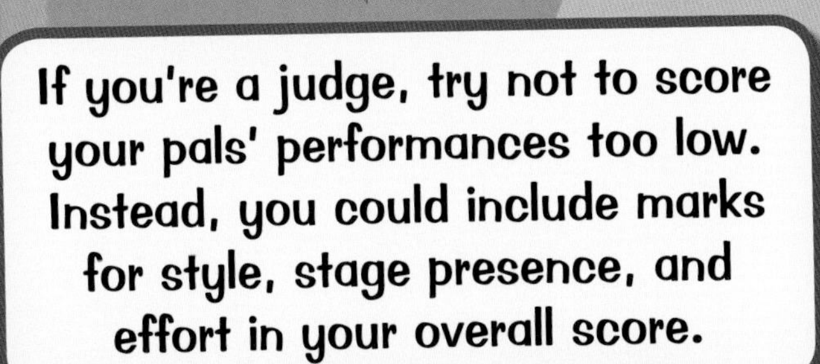

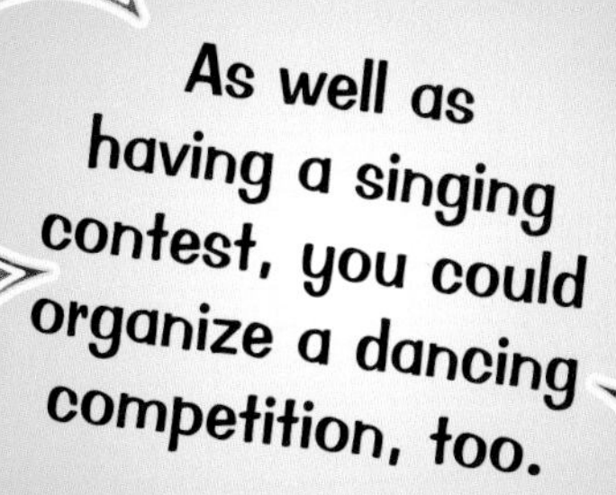

Don't forget to build up all the positive things about the performances. You might even find a singing starlet in your gang.

If you're the singer, just relax and go for it. It doesn't really matter if you can hold a tune or not. This game is just for fun!

Dance routines

It's time to put on your dancing shoes and bust some serious moves.

If you or any of your guests are really good at dancing, try making up your own routines for everyone else to learn and copy. If you need some ideas, watch a few music videos. Still stuck? Try out the dance steps below. Put them in any order you like, match your rhythm to the music, and you'll be in boogie heaven!

ONE

- Put your hands behind your back.
- Cross your right leg over your left.
- Step to the left with your left leg and clap your hands in front of you at the same time.

TWO

- Cross your right arm over your chest and touch your left shoulder. Step forward with your right leg at the same time.
- Cross your left arm over your chest and touch your right shoulder. Step forward with your left leg at the same time.
- Drop both arms down to your sides and jump backward.

THREE

- Turn to face the right and push your right foot forward.
- Bend your arms at the elbows.
- Swing your hips from side to side and move your arms with them.
- Jump around to face the left and repeat the same moves on that side.

FOUR

- Stand with your feet apart.
- Hold your left arm straight down by your side and splay your fingers.
- Point your right arm straight up in the air.
- In one smooth move, swap your arms over, so the left one is in the air and the right by your side.

FIVE

- Step to the right with your right foot. As you step, swing your right arm up and out to the side. Click your fingers.
- Step your other foot across to the right, and swing your arm back down again as you move.
- Do this twice, and then step back to the left.

Chart toppers!

Who will be the first to take their hot new single right to the top of the charts? Play this game with a friend or two and find out.

6
7
You're late for your recording studio appointment. Miss a turn.
8
9
10
11
How to play
Use pennies or nickels as counters and another coin for a dice. Take turns to throw the dice coin and move around the board. Move two places if the coin lands head-side up and one place if it lands on tails. The first player to reach FINISH is the chart-topping winner.
12
A talent scout thinks your voice is amazing and immediately signs you up to his record label. Move ahead 5 spaces.
28
29
30
Finish!
13
14
18
Your single enters the charts at number 6. Have another turn to celebrate.
17
16
Disaster strikes! You get a really bad sore throat and lose your voice! Throw heads to move on.
15

word games

Looking for something to do? How about trying one of these cool word games with a friend or two?

Straight face

First choose someone to be "it." The others pick a phrase for the player who is "it" and then ask her questions that she must answer with the chosen phrase. For instance, you could choose the phrase "a stinky sock" and then ask your friend questions such as "what do you clean your teeth with?" or "what do you eat for breakfast?". If she giggles, she's out!

Alphabet celebs

Go through the alphabet with your friends, taking turns to name a celeb that begins with each letter. You could choose to say first names or surnames or both—it's up to you. Anyone who can't think of a celeb that begins with a certain letter is out of the game!

Crazy alphabet

This game can get seriously silly! To start the game, someone says, "When I was on my way to school I saw..." and adds something beginning with the letter "a," for instance, "an amazing acrobatic anteater." The next person repeats the sentence and then adds something beginning with "b"... "when I was on my way to school I saw an amazing acrobatic anteater and a baby baboon" and so on. See if you can make it all the way through the alphabet!

Boredom busters

It's so cool being a girl! Check out all the fab things you can do to entertain your best pals.

SCRAPBOOK CHALLENGE

Instead of throwing out old movie tickets, candy wrappers, and old photos, create a "Me and My Friends" scrapbook for all your fantastic, girlie memorabilia.

GAME PALS

Make up a cool new game using sports equipment, such as tennis rackets or footballs. Make a list of the rules so you can keep it for the next time you want to play the same game.

CUSTOM CRAZY

Ask your pals to each bring around an old tank top or T-shirt to your house. Then have fun decorating all of the tops using fabric glitter pens. Why not autograph your designs, too?

MUSICAL MANIA

Watch your fave movie, then turn it into a musical by making up songs and dance moves about the movie. Practice your routines, then perform your show in front of your families.

BEDROOM BAND

Make your own bedroom band by each learning an instrument and practicing every week. Any instruments count—from recorders to maracas, they all sound cool!

HAIR FLAIR

Flick through some mags for ideas, then give each other as many new hairstyles as you can. Take photos to help you remember the best styles.

"The best piece of advice I've ever gotten is to trust myself and go for my dreams." Sarah Michelle Gellar

BOOK BABES

Have a go at writing your own "Girls Only" novel. Take it in turns to each write a page. Don't forget to read each other's work as you go. It could be a bestseller!

Best buddies

Okay, so you know that you and your pals are fab friends, but are you more like Shopping Sisters or Karaoke Queens? Try this quiz to find out.

1 It's Saturday, what are you all going to do?

A Make up dance moves
B Play sports
C Customize clothes
D Hit the stores

2 Which item of clothing do you wear the most?

A Party top
B Sneakers
C Funky T-shirt
D Jeans

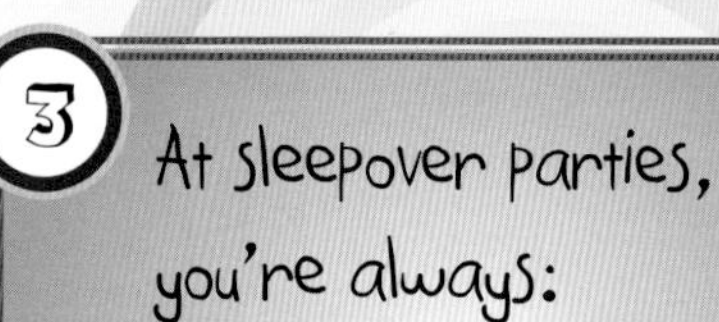

3 At sleepover parties, you're always:

A Singing
B Dancing
C Reading
D Sleeping

4 On weekends, you spend your time:

A Making up songs
B Swimming
C Creating collages
D Hanging out at the mall

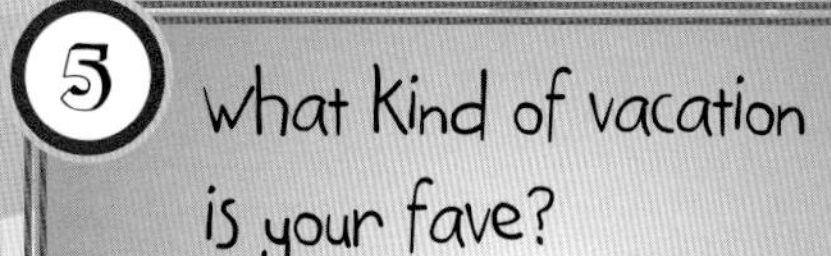

5 What kind of vacation is your fave?

A Beach
B Activity
C Arty
D Shopping

6 If you were an animal, you'd be a:

A Puppy
B Dolphin
C Bunny
D Kitten

7 You and your buddies dream of being:

A Pop stars
B Athletes
C Fashion designers
D Models

Now find out your gang's group personality. First, count up how many As, Bs, Cs, and Ds you've got, then check out the results.

Results

Mostly As = Karaoke queens
Mostly Bs = Sporting stars
Mostly Cs = Creative cuties
Mostly Ds = Shopping Sisters

"Mary-Kate is always there when I need her. She's my best friend."
Ashley Olsen

DIY DIVAS

If you like making things, turn your sleepover into an arty party! Try at one or two of these cool activities and you'll also be creating something that shows your friends how much they mean to you.

Cool cases

Ask each of your guests to bring along an old pillowcase from home. Slip a piece of cardboard or a carrier bag inside to stop the paint from seeping through to the back. Gather together some fabric paints, fabric pens, and brushes. Take turns designing a small area on each pillowcase, then pass the pillowcase onto the next person. You should all end up with a customized pillowcase that everyone's had a hand in designing.

Top tees

Take the idea above but instead of adding your art to a pillowcase, do it on a T-shirt. If you go for baggy, oversized tees (try Dad-sized ones!), then once the paint dries, you could all wear them as nightshirts at your sleepover.

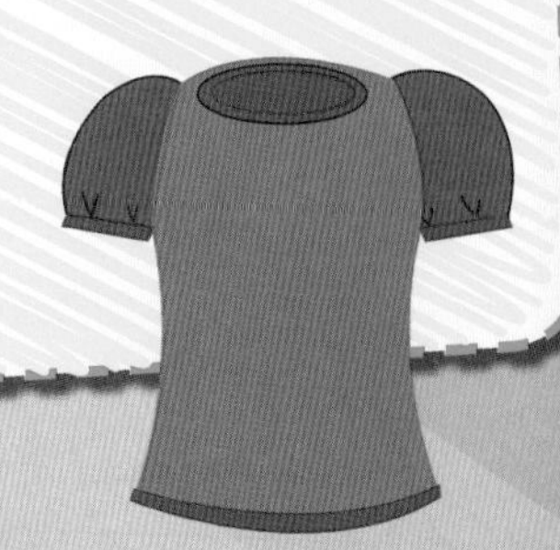

Awesome autographs

Decorate the outside of a small, plain notebook with glitter, fake fur, sequins, buttons, ribbon trim—anything you like—to turn it into a special autograph book. Then, pass it around and get each of your friends to write you a message and sign their name inside.

Perfect purses

Recycle old jeans, denim skirts, or denim jackets to make really cute denim purses and bags.

Cut out a rectangle of denim fabric and fold the bottom edge over so it's around three-quarters of the way up the strip.

Glue or stitch the side edges together and then fold the top section down to make your purse flap.

You can hold it closed with Velcro™ or a button and then decorate with glitzy, girly art materials.

To make your purse a bag, just attach a length of ribbon or cord at either side as a strap.

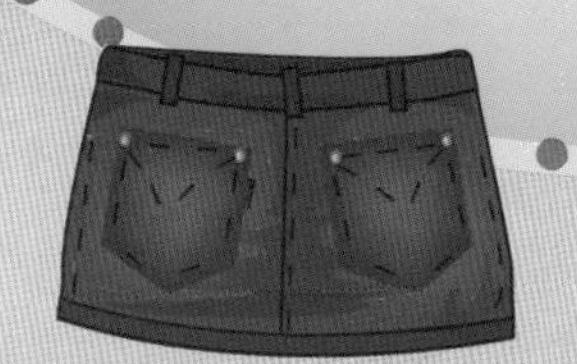

Happy hands

Look at your pals' palms and read the following pages to find out what they might mean.

A long middle finger means your friend is a really brainy babe.

A long index finger means your friend is a creative chick.

If your buddy has a long ring finger, she's fab at keeping secrets.

Does your pal have a square-shaped thumb? If so, she loves planning cool stuff to do!

A curved heart line means your pal is very confident.

A long head line suggests your best friend has got a great memory.

A long and deep life line may mean that your friend is a deep thinker.

If your friend's heart line and head line are close together, it means she's lucky.

Secret destiny

Try this cool quiz to find out what the future has in store for you and your sleepover pals.

1. What's the best thing about sleepovers?

a)	Just spending time hanging out with your friends
b)	Settling down to tell spooky stories
c)	Giving your pals cool makeovers
d)	Singing your fave karaoke tunes

2. Which of these do you never leave home without?

d)	Your lip gloss and a mirror
a)	Your cell phone
c)	A book or magazine
b)	Something to draw with

3. What would your friends say is your worst quality?

b)	You fiddle with things
d)	You're sometimes a show-off
c)	You're always daydreaming
a)	You can be really mushy

4. Look at these pictures. Which one do you like best?

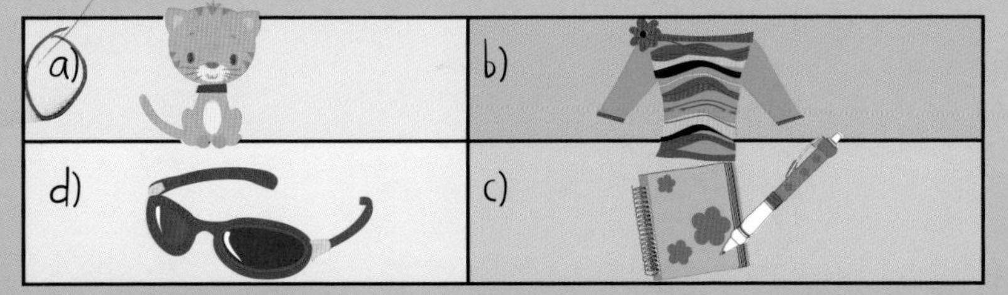

Mostly As

Kind, caring, and patient, you'd make an amazing veterinarian. You love anything that's cute and girly and you're passionate about animals. Your calm, loyal nature and super advice mean anyone would be happy to have you as a friend.

Mostly Bs

Funky, creative, and stylish, you could be a great fashion designer. You're crazy about clothes and accessories and love customizing things so they're totally unique. With an enormous wardrobe and tons of cool style ideas, it's no wonder your friends love you!

Mostly Cs

Bright, imaginative, and hard-working, you'd be an awesome author. You love books and reading and are a real day-dreamer. Although you can seem a little shy at first, you're a great friend and hilarious once people get to know you.

Mostly Ds

Confident and talented, you'd make an amazing actress. You're happiest being at the center of the attention and shine under the spotlight. The life and soul of any party, you've got tons of friends who always have a great time when you're around.

BEST FRIENDS' CHALLENGE

You're great friends but how well do you really know each other? Take the test and find out!

How to play

- Pass around some paper and a pencil or pen to each player.
- Take it in turns to be the quizmaster and ask each of the questions about yourself. Everyone else writes down the answers—it's up to you to make sure there's no consulting or cheating!
- When you've asked all of the questions, go back to the start and give out your answers so the other players can mark their papers.
- Check their scores against the list below and hand out treats or forfeits to the people who deserve them.
- The winner—and the best best friend—is the person with the highest overall score at the end of the game.

How to score

Score two points for each correct answer. If someone has part of an answer right—for instance, if they know your mom's name, but can't remember what your dad is called for question 7—you can award them just one point.

Questions

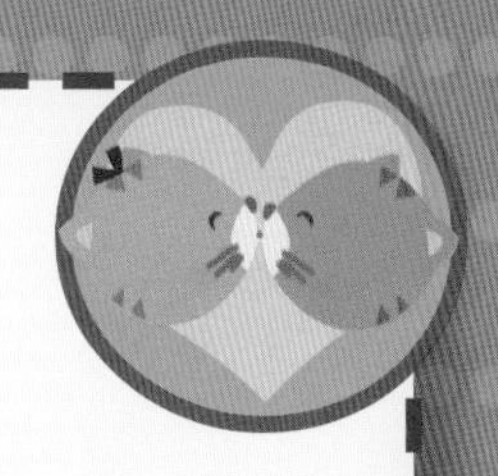

1. What's my middle name?
2. What do I want to be when I leave school?
3. Who's my secret crush?
4. What's my favorite book?
5. If I could be any famous person, who would I most like to be?
6. What's my horoscope sign?
7. What are my mom and dad called?
8. If I could have any animal as a pet, what would I choose?

If your friend scores:

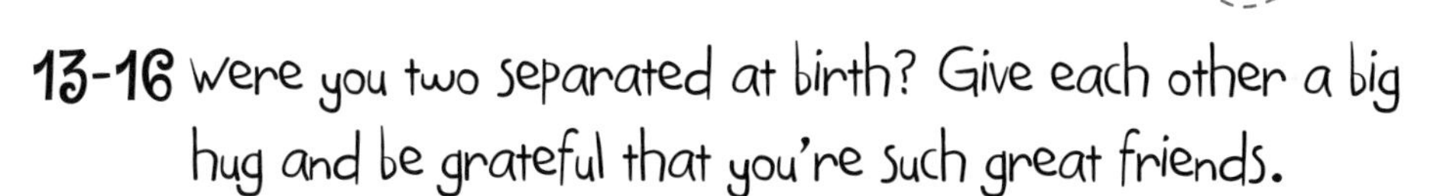

13-16 Were you two separated at birth? Give each other a big hug and be grateful that you're such great friends.

9-12 Wow—she knows tons about you! Get together for a good gossip soon and fill her in on the few things she got wrong.

5-8 Hmm, could do better. But instead of being ticked, use it as a great excuse for regular heart-to-heart girly chats from now on.

0-4 Ouch!—you're hardly bosom buddies! You need to spend more time getting to know each other. You'll soon be the best of friends!

mini makeovers

Kiss 'n' makeup

When it comes to makeup, less is most definitely more. Follow these cool makeup tips, and have fun experimenting with different looks.

Eyes

DO

...use light, shimmery eye colors and sweep them across your eyelids with a fingertip or small brush.

...try using clear mascara to separate and define your lashes.

DON'T

... spread the color all the way up to your brow bone.

...pick dark-colored mascara, which can look really clumpy and give you smudgy panda eyes.

Cheeks

DO

...look out for cheek tint that comes in a gel or cream.

...smile, and apply blusher really lightly over the apples that appear at the top of your cheeks.

DON'T

...go for powder blusher. It can be cakey-looking on young skin.

...forget to rub your blusher in to blend the edges. Stripes of color or little round circles are not cool.

Lips

DO

...go for gloss over lipstick. You could even go for a tinted lip balm.

...blot your gloss by pressing your lips onto a tissue. Add a second coat on top for super-staying power.

DON'T

...be afraid to mix colors together. Blend them on your hand first.

...ever be tempted to use lip liner, or apply lip gloss outside the natural line of your lips.

Nails

DO

...try all kinds of different nail colors.

...get a friend to paint your nails, then do hers in return. They'll be neater than when you do it yourself.

DON'T

...wear really dark shades for more than a few hours at a time. They can stain your nails.

... bite them! It's so not cool!

Snap!

Say cheese

Now you're made up, take it in turns to do your best model pose! Grab a camera and snap some super model pics.

Recipes aren't just for eating—try these yummy treats and let your skin do the scoffing in your personal sleepover spa.

Making your own beauty products is a blast but it can be a little messy. Grab a stack of old towels instead of using Mom's best, wear PJs, a bathrobe, or an old T-shirt, and make sure you don't get the goodies in too many places they shouldn't go!

Face pack

Pssst... Look for rose water in the baking section of your local supermarket.

(This recipe makes enough for six people)

You will need:

- 4 egg whites
- 4 tablespoons honey
- 12 tablespoons powdered milk

What to do:

- Add the egg whites to a mixing bowl and beat them with a fork for about a minute until they go frothy. Stir in the other ingredients and mix thoroughly.
- Carefully spread onto your face and get your guests to do the same. Keep it away from the skin around your eyes.
- Lie back and relax for 15-20 minutes while the mask works its magic. Stick on a CD, or have fun talking as you're waiting.
- Rinse off with warm water, then pat your skin dry with a towel.
- Admire your gorgeous reflection and sparkling skin in the mirror.

Quick fixes

If you want a few speedy spa ideas, give these a go:

- Mash up a banana or an avocado, lie back, and spread over your face. After 15 minutes, rinse off with warm water and pat dry.
- Chop a lemon or lime in half and rub it over any rough patches of skin on your knees or elbows. Avoid touching broken skin though, as it might sting.
- Slice up some cucumber, lie down, and close your eyes. Rest a cucumber slice on each of your lids to soothe and refresh tired peepers (perfect when you've been awake gossiping most of the night!).

marvelous manicure

Every stylish chick has perfect nails. Check out these nail care tips.

For fun nails:

1. File your nails into shape with an emery board.

2. Soak your fingers in a bowl of warm water and a squeeze of lemon juice to cleanse and soften them. After a few minutes, pat them dry with a towel.

3. Massage some hand lotion into your hands or get a friend to do it for you. Then wipe your nails with nail polish remover.

4. Now you're ready to choose your nail color and start painting. First brush down the middle of your nail, then add two strips of color to either side of it. Add another layer when the first one is dry.

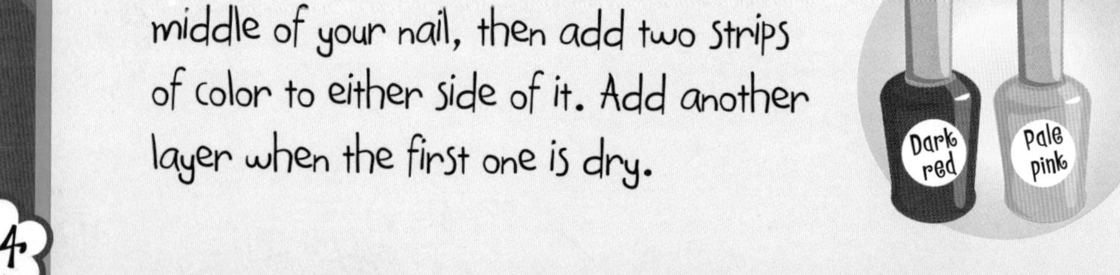

Get creative with some nail art. Take turns to transform each of your friends' nails with these cool designs.

TOP TIP
Keep your nail polish in the refrigerator to help it stay in tip-top condition. Also, this should make the polish dry more quickly on your nails.

Two-tone shades

Brush on two coats of pale-colored nail varnish. Let these coats dry, then paint a second, darker shade diagonally across each of your nails.

Stylish stickers

For a simple, funky nail makeover, look out for nail stickers or transfers. You can press them on top of your painted or naked nails for an instant, arty style.

Gorgeous gems

Varnish with your favorite nail color and let dry. Pick a contrasting shade, then paint on five tiny blobs in a circle on your nail. Add a sixth blob in the center, then press a nail gem on top. Repeat until you've created a full set of flowery fingernails.

Avoid applying and removing polish more than twice a week to keep your nails strong and healthy.

Cool colors

The colors you wear can make a difference to the way you look. Take this quick test to find out which shades suit your coloring the best.

IF YOUR SKIN IS: pale and pink or peachy

IF YOUR SKIN IS: brown or black

IF YOUR SKIN IS: fair with freckles

IF YOUR SKIN IS: olive or honey colored

YOUR TONE IS: cool

YOUR TONE IS warm

TOP TIP:

Work out your coloring with your friends. Look at all your favorite colored tops together, then take turns trying them on to find out which colors suit you more than others.

IF YOUR HAIR IS:
blonde or light brown
AND YOUR EYES ARE:
blue, gray, or light brown

YOUR COLORING IS:
Bright
TRY WEARING: raspberry red, pale pink, yellow, and turquoise
BEST FOR BEAUTY:
soft pink blusher and fruity lip balm

IF YOUR HAIR IS:
dark brown or black
AND YOUR EYES ARE:
dark blue, green, or brown

YOUR COLORING IS:
Chilled
TRY WEARING: emerald green, fuschia pink, scarlet, and silver
BEST FOR BEAUTY: glittery eye shadow and cherry-red lip gloss

IF YOUR HAIR IS:
auburn, brown, or strawberry blonde
AND YOUR EYES ARE:
blue, green, or hazel

YOUR COLORING IS:
Spicy
TRY WEARING: chocolate brown, leafy green, and orangey red
BEST FOR BEAUTY: green eye shadow and chocolatey lip balm

IF YOUR HAIR IS:
blonde, dark brown, or black
AND YOUR EYES ARE:
green, blue, or brown

YOUR COLORING IS:
Fresh
TRY WEARING: lilac, coral pink, pale green, and aqua
BEST FOR BEAUTY: iridescent cheek shimmer and lilac lip gloss

Get the look!

Do you and your pals dream of being fashion designers? Show off all your fave looks right here...

Place a picture or drawing of your fave look here!

This look rocks because: ....

I'd wear it to the: ....

....

My best friend ....
(write the name of your pal here)
would look fab in this.

This look is called: ....

It's cool because: ....

....

It's perfect for: ....

....

Place a picture or drawing of your fave look here!

I love this outfit! It would look great on:

....

My friend.................... should
(write the name of your pal here)

wear it to: ....

Place a picture or drawing of your fave look here!

Place a picture or drawing of your fave look here!

I wish I had this outfit. I'd wear it to: ....

My fave thing about it is:

....

....

My name is: ....

I am: .... years old

I am: .... feet/inches tall

My shoe size is: ....

Today I'm wearing: ....

For parties, I normally wear: ....

My hairstyle at the moment is: ....

I buy most of my clothes at: ....

The last thing I bought was: ....

Fashion is always changing. Keep a record of your fashion changes with this fun questionnaire. Photocopy these pages, fill in your answers, and get each of your pals to do the same.

The pop act I get style inspiration from is: ....

My favorite supermodel is: ....

The trendiest girl at school is: ....

The magazine I read the most is: ....

If I could be any celebrity, I would be: ....

I have a crush on: ....

I love it when he wears his: ....

My top style secret is: ....

Fashion show

Who will be the first to strut their stuff down the catwalk at the International Fashion Show? Play this fun game with a friend or two.

9 The makeup artist has left all her brushes at home! Miss a turn while she finds her spare set.

10

11

How to play

Use pennies or nickels as counters and another coin as a dice. Take turns to throw the dice coin and move around the board. Move two places if the coin lands head-side up and one place if it lands on tails. The first player to reach the catwalk wins.

4 You arrive for your dress fitting an hour early. Move ahead one place.

3

12 Oh no! Your outfit is the wrong size! Move back five places.

13

26
25
24
27
23
28
22
29
You trip over
as you race toward
the catwalk.
Go back to the
start.
21
20
Your dress rips as
you put it on but you
customize the
tear with some
funky ribbons.
Take another turn.
30
Finish!
19
17
Your hair stylist
gives you the
perfect look.
Move ahead four
places.
18
14
15
16

What's your FASHION STYLE?

Do you always manage to look fabulous whatever the occasion—or are you a bit of a fashion disaster? Take this test to discover your true fashion style.

START

Do you like getting glammed up for parties?
YES / NO

Do you like customizing your own clothes?
YES / NO

Do you swap fashion ideas with your best friends?
YES / NO

Do you like to copy all the latest trends?
NO / YES

Do you sometimes buy the same clothes as your friends?
NO / YES

Do you sometimes borrow things from your friends' wardrobes to complete your outfit?
NO / YES

Do your accessories always match what you're wearing perfectly?
YES / NO

Do you have a lot of cool hats and belts to funk up your outfit?

YES / NO

Are you good at giving your friends makeovers?

YES / NO

Do you try to find main street versions of your fave celeb's clothes?

YES / NO

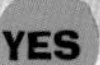

Do you mix and match your clothes to create unique looks?

YES / NO

Do you wear all the latest styles whether they suit you or not?

YES

Fashion guru: There's not a lot you don't know about fashion. You definitely know what's hot from what's not. You always look amazing because you know what suits you, and your friends really appreciate your fashion advice.

Stylish sista: You've got a cool style all of your own. You get ideas from the season's hottest looks, then adapt them to suit your own personal style. You're pretty creative and always manage to make things that you've had for years look completely up to date!

Copycat: You're not really sure what suits you, so you tend to copy whatever your friends and your fave celebs are wearing. Ask your friends to give you some pointers and then you can create a look all of your own.

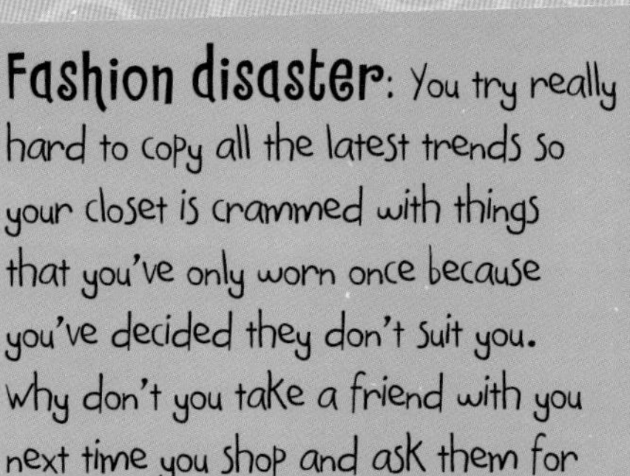

Fashion disaster: You try really hard to copy all the latest trends so your closet is crammed with things that you've only worn once because you've decided they don't suit you. Why don't you take a friend with you next time you shop and ask them for some fashion tips?

Superstar Style

Capricorn (Dec 22–Jan 20)
You are: ambitious and enthusiastic
Dress up in: chic skirts
Dress down in: funky tennis shoes
Lucky color: brown
Top shopping friend: Virgo

Aries (Mar 21–Apr 20)
You are: energetic and adventurous
Dress up in: high heels
Dress down in: tracksuit pants
Lucky color: silver
Top shopping friend: Sagittarius

Aquarius (Jan 21–Feb 19)
You are: arty and intelligent
Dress up in: smart pants
Dress down in: cute beanie hats
Lucky color: purple
Top shopping friend: Gemini

Taurus (Apr 21–May 21)
You are: loyal and funny
Dress up in: cool jackets
Dress down in: funky flip-flops
Lucky color: green
Top shopping friend: Libra

Pisces (Feb 20–Mar 20)
You are: dreamy and generous
Dress up in: strappy tops
Dress down in: cool cords
Lucky color: turquoise
Top shopping friend: Cancer

Gemini (May 22–Jun 21)
You are: cheerful and chatty
Dress up in: anything with sequins
Dress down in: tank tops
Lucky color: white
Top shopping friend: Aquarius

Check out your fashion horoscope, then sneak a peek at your best friend's, too.

Cancer (Jun 22-Jul 23)
You are: Kind and honest
Dress up in: funky accessories
Dress down in: Snug sweaters
Lucky color: red
Top shopping friend: Pisces

Libra (Sept 24-Oct 23)
You are: stylish and outgoing
Dress up in: billowy tops
Dress down in: comfy jeans
Lucky color: pink
Top shopping friend: Taurus

Leo (Jul 24-Aug 23)
You are: confident and friendly
Dress up in: stylish dresses
Dress down in: layered T-shirts
Lucky color: yellow
Top shopping friend: Scorpio

Scorpio (Oct 24-Nov 22)
You are: mysterious and creative
Dress up in: anything in velvet
Dress down in: logo T-shirts
Lucky color: orange
Top shopping friend: Leo

Virgo (Aug 24-Sept 23)
You are: tidy and thoughtful
Dress up in: glitzy shoes
Dress down in: trendy sweatshirt
Lucky color: indigo
Top shopping friend: Capricorn

Sagittarius (Nov 23-Dec 21)
You are: fun-loving and imaginative
Dress up in: sparkly jeans
Dress down in: comfy boots
Lucky color: blue
Top shopping friend: Aries

Your sleepover style

Are you first to get up and dance, or always on hand to provide a few laughs? Work your way through this cool flowchart and find out.

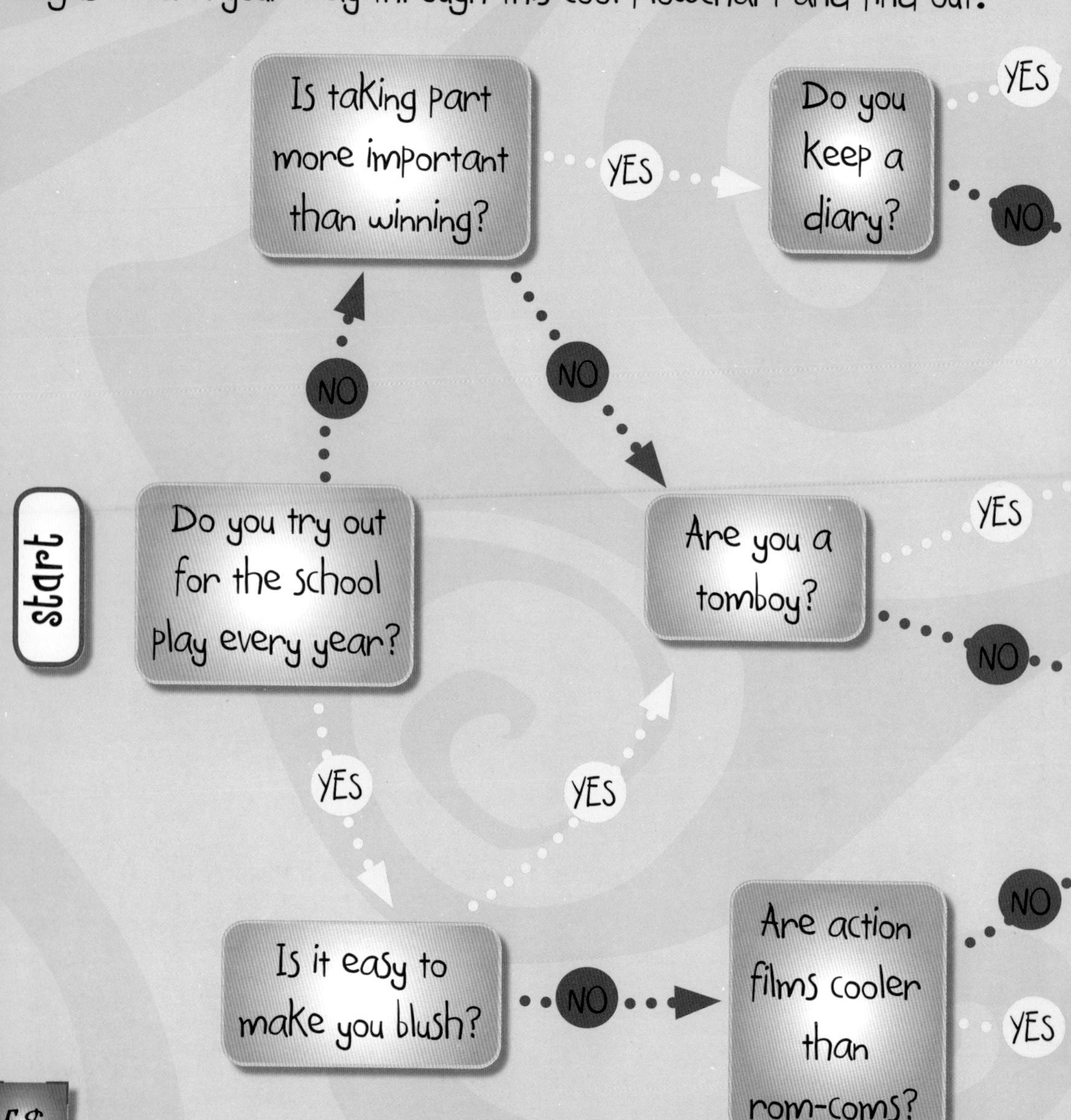

YOUR SLEEPOVER STYLE IS . . .
Super-organized and cheerful with tons of enthusiasm, you're most likely to arrive first.
TRY THIS: Make welcome drinks with umbrellas and pieces of floating fruit.

Have you ever been scolded for giggling in class?

NO

YES

YOUR SLEEPOVER STYLE IS . . .
You're a real joker and always ready to have fun, which means you're the most likely to try a silly hairstyle.
TRY THIS: Organize a crazy hairstyle competition and take a photo of the results.

Is pink your favorite color?

NO

YES

YOUR SLEEPOVER STYLE IS . . .
Cute, girly, and a sensitive softie at heart, you're most likely to scream at a spooky story.
TRY THIS: Bake a batch of heart-shaped cookies with pink icing for everyone to share.

Have you ever dreamed of being a popstar?

NO

YES

YOUR SLEEPOVER STYLE IS . . .
You're a little ball of energy and love being the center of attention, which means you're most likely to be first on the dance floor.
TRY THIS: Make up a dance routine and teach it to everyone else.

Going home

There's no reason the fun should stop once the sun comes up. Make the very end of your sleepover just as cool as the rest of it!

Fast food

Ask your parents if you can make your own breakfast. Try a big bowl of fruit salad with some frozen yogurt, or cut toast into cute shapes with cookie cutters and add any spread you like. Cocoa or fruit juice are perfect breakfast drinks, or try the recipe below and whip up a cool milkshake.

Bananutter Breakfast Smoothie

(These quantities serve one person, so multiply them by the number of guests you're serving.)

You will need:

- 1 cup of milk
- Half a banana, sliced
- Cocoa powder
- 1 tablespoon peanut butter
- Few drops vanilla extract

What you do:

Put the milk, banana, peanut butter, and vanilla extract into a blender and blend until very smooth. Drop one or two ice cubes into a glass, add the blended mixture, and then shake some cocoa powder on top to finish off.

Do me a favor

Party favors—the little goodie bags you give to your guests as they leave—are a great way of saying "thanks for coming and making my sleepover so much fun." They don't need to cost a fortune, especially if you're happy to spend a little bit of time before the sleepover making some cute 'n' easy gifts. Check out the suggestions below if you're stuck for ideas:

- Buy a pack of inexpensive plain hair clips and decorate them with nail polish, glitter, beads, and sequins.
- Print off promise-vouchers on your computer, decorate them with felt tips, and punch holes at the edge of each one. Thread ribbon through to turn them into little books. Your promises could be things like helping out with homework, lending her your fave top, sharing a magazine you both like, or making her some yummy cookies.
- Turn cheap pens into something awesome by dipping them into glue and then rolling in glitter. Stick a feather to the end, and let the pen dry before you wrap it up.

Pssst...

When you're picking out DVD movies to watch at your sleepover, set one aside for the morning. It's the perfect way to chill out between breakfast and everyone's parents arriving to take them home.